E6

THE ROYAL
HORTICULTURAL SOCIETY
DIARY 1993

Watercolours by Dorothy B. Martin

FRANCES LINCOLN

Frances Lincoln Limited
Apollo Works, 5 Charlton Kings Road, London NW5 2SB

The Royal Horticultural Society Diary 1993
Copyright © Frances Lincoln Limited 1992
Illustrations copyright © The Royal Horticultural Society 1992

Astronomical information reproduced, with permission, from
data supplied by HM Nautical Almanac office, copyright ©
Science and Engineering Research Council

Design by Roger Walton Studio

British Library Cataloguing in Publication Data
A catalogue record for this book is available from the British
Library.

ISBN 0-7112-0752-6

Printed in Hong Kong

First Frances Lincoln edition: July 1992

A note on plant names
Correct modern plant names are given, while those Dorothy
Martin used are shown in brackets. Where necessary, family
names have also been corrected and hence these may differ
from those given by Miss Martin.

Year Planner

1993

JANUARY	FEBRUARY	MARCH	APRIL
M T W T F S S	M T W T F S S	M T W T F S S	M T W T F S S
1 2 3	1 2 3 4 5 6 7	1 2 3 4 5 6 7	1 2 3 4
4 5 6 7 8 9 10	8 9 10 11 12 13 14	8 9 10 11 12 13 14	5 6 7 8 9 10 11
11 12 13 14 15 16 17	15 16 17 18 19 20 21	15 16 17 18 19 20 21	12 13 14 15 16 17 18
18 19 20 21 22 23 24	22 23 24 25 26 27 28	22 23 24 25 26 27 28	19 20 21 22 23 24 25
25 26 27 28 29 30 31		29 30 31	26 27 28 29 30

MAY	JUNE	JULY	AUGUST
M T W T F S S	M T W T F S S	M T W T F S S	M T W T F S S
1 2	1 2 3 4 5 6	1 2 3 4	1
3 4 5 6 7 8 9	7 8 9 10 11 12 13	5 6 7 8 9 10 11	2 3 4 5 6 7 8
10 11 12 13 14 15 16	14 15 16 17 18 19 20	12 13 14 15 16 17 18	9 10 11 12 13 14 15
17 18 19 20 21 22 23	21 22 23 24 25 26 27	19 20 21 22 23 24 25	16 17 18 19 20 21 22
24 25 26 27 28 29 30	28 29 30	26 27 28 29 30 31	23 24 25 26 27 28 29
31			30 31

SEPTEMBER	OCTOBER	NOVEMBER	DECEMBER
M T W T F S S	M T W T F S S	M T W T F S S	M T W T F S S
1 2 3 4 5	1 2 3	1 2 3 4 5 6 7	1 2 3 4 5
6 7 8 9 10 11 12	4 5 6 7 8 9 10	8 9 10 11 12 13 14	6 7 8 9 10 11 12
13 14 15 16 17 18 19	11 12 13 14 15 16 17	15 16 17 18 19 20 21	13 14 15 16 17 18 19
20 21 22 23 24 25 26	18 19 20 21 22 23 24	22 23 24 25 26 27 28	20 21 22 23 24 25 26
27 28 29 30	25 26 27 28 29 30 31	29 30	27 28 29 30 31

1994

JANUARY	FEBRUARY	MARCH	APRIL
M T W T F S S	M T W T F S S	M T W T F S S	M T W T F S S
1 2	1 2 3 4 5 6	1 2 3 4 5 6	1 2 3
3 4 5 6 7 8 9	7 8 9 10 11 12 13	7 8 9 10 11 12 13	4 5 6 7 8 9 10
10 11 12 13 14 15 16	14 15 16 17 18 19 20	14 15 16 17 18 19 20	11 12 13 14 15 16 17
17 18 19 20 21 22 23	21 22 23 24 25 26 27	21 22 23 24 25 26 27	18 19 20 21 22 23 24
24 25 26 27 28 29 30	28	28 29 30 31	25 26 27 28 29 30
31			

MAY	JUNE	JULY	AUGUST
M T W T F S S	M T W T F S S	M T W T F S S	M T W T F S S
1	1 2 3 4 5	1 2 3	1 2 3 4 5 6 7
2 3 4 5 6 7 8	6 7 8 9 10 11 12	4 5 6 7 8 9 10	8 9 10 11 12 13 14
9 10 11 12 13 14 15	13 14 15 16 17 18 19	11 12 13 14 15 16 17	15 16 17 18 19 20 21
16 17 18 19 20 21 22	20 21 22 23 24 25 26	18 19 20 21 22 23 24	22 23 24 25 26 27 28
23 24 25 26 27 28 29	27 28 29 30	25 26 27 28 29 30 31	29 30 31
30 31			

SEPTEMBER	OCTOBER	NOVEMBER	DECEMBER
M T W T F S S	M T W T F S S	M T W T F S S	M T W T F S S
1 2 3 4	1 2	1 2 3 4 5 6	1 2 3 4
5 6 7 8 9 10 11	3 4 5 6 7 8 9	7 8 9 10 11 12 13	5 6 7 8 9 10 11
12 13 14 15 16 17 18	10 11 12 13 14 15 16	14 15 16 17 18 19 20	12 13 14 15 16 17 18
19 20 21 22 23 24 25	17 18 19 20 21 22 23	21 22 23 24 25 26 27	19 20 21 22 23 24 25
26 27 28 29 30	24 25 26 27 28 29 30	28 29 30	26 27 28 29 30 31
	31		

Introduction

Dorothy B. Martin (1882-1949) completed over three hundred drawings for a projected flora of the British Isles during her time at Roedean School, where she was art mistress from 1916 to 1946. She found the models for her charming illustrations in the Sussex countryside around Roedean, in the Lake District where the school was evacuated during the Second World War, and in specimens specially sent to her. Her love of nature and singleminded pursuit of her art is recalled by a friend who remembers her sitting calmly in the School's studio to paint a flower sent to her, surrounded by the detritus of the recent removal from Keswick to Brighton; 'For, my dear,' she said, 'the flower may be dead tomorrow, but this mess will still be here'.

Had Miss Martin completed her flora, from the artistic point of view it would easily have rivalled the work of her slightly elder contemporary, the Revd Keble Martin, whose *Concise British Flora*, eventually published in 1965, is the best-known and most reprinted illustrated British flora of the twentieth century. The two artists were very different in style, but both were rooted in the Edwardian context of botanical illustration. This manifested itself, at about the time when Miss Martin was starting her teaching career at Roedean, in the publication of three separate British floras; each defined a different set of stylistic choices, which provided the background against which Miss Martin began her work.

Of the three rival floras the weakest was C. E. Moss's *Cambridge British Flora* (1914-20), with line drawings by E. W. Hunneybun. The model for Keble Martin's book was *Wild Flowers of the British Isles*, with illustrations by H. Isabel Adams (two volumes, 1910); her plates, executed in very pastel colours, were compositions of several species. The third work was *British Flowering Plants*, with text by G. S. Bougler and illustrations by Mrs Henry Perrin (three volumes, 1914). The influence of Mrs Perrin's watercolour washes (not always successful in the published reproductions), and her concentration on individual specimens, can be seen in Dorothy Martin's work. Another characteristic the two artists share is the accurate depiction of flaws in the specimen, as opposed to the idealised representations of Adams and Keble Martin.

On Dorothy Martin's death, her twin sister Margaret, as executor, sought the advice of the Royal Horticultural Society's Librarian, W. T. Stearn, about the value of the drawings. A formal notice of acceptance followed Dr Stearn's visit to Brighton to inspect the paintings to see 'if they proved of a quality to merit their inclusion in the Lindley Library'. Dr Stearn was the co-author of Wilfred Blunt's book *The Art of Botanical Illustration* (1950), which made the first public reference to Dorothy Martin's 'several hundred fine sheets of British wild flowers'; he also corrected the botanical names on the sheets. A condition was attached to the bequest, allowing the drawings to be exhibited outside the Society's own rooms (not a normal practice at that time); some of the drawings were exhibited at the Festival of Arts in Auckland, New Zealand, in May 1954.

With this volume, fifty-five of Dorothy Martin's finest illustrations are published for the first time. Readers now have an opportunity to judge her drawings for themselves.

Brent Elliott
The Royal Horticultural Society

Cirsium eriophorum (formerly called *Carduus eriophorus*), woolly thistle,
a member of the Compositae family

Compositæ

Carduus eriophorus
Woolly Thistle.

(2 to 3 feet.)

December 1992

MONDAY 28

TUESDAY 29

WEDNESDAY 30

THURSDAY 31

FRIDAY 1   **January** 1993   *New Year's Day Holiday*
           ☽ First Quarter

SATURDAY 2

SUNDAY 3

Galanthus nivalis, the snowdrop,
with *Leucojum aestivum*, the summer snowflake
and *Narcissus pseudonarcissus*, the daffodil or Lent lily,
members of the Amaryllidaceae family

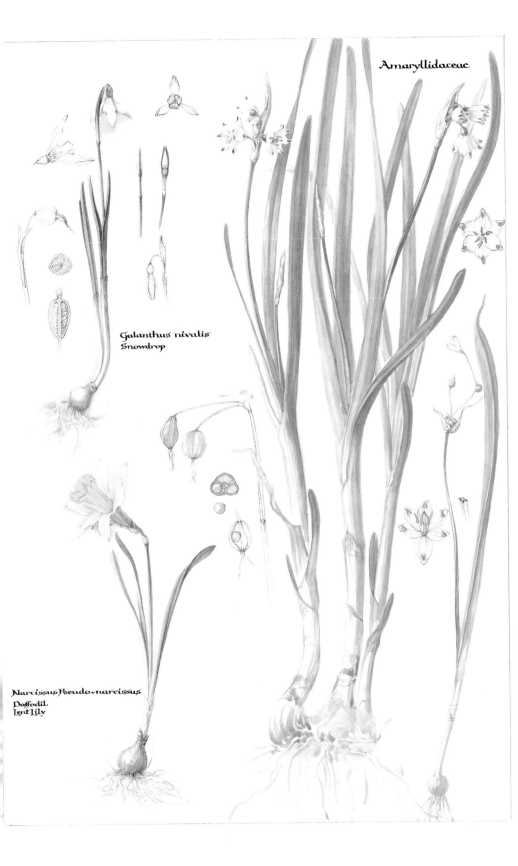

Amaryllidaceae

Galanthus nivalis
Snowdrop

Narcissus Pseudo-narcissus
Daffodil
Lent Lily

MONDAY 4
Holiday, Scotland

TUESDAY 5

WEDNESDAY 6
Epiphany

THURSDAY 7

FRIDAY 8 ○ Full Moon

SATURDAY 9

SUNDAY 10

Typha latifolia, great reedmace or cat's-tail,
a member of the Typhaceae family

Typhaceae

Typha latifolia
Great Reedmace,
Cat's-tail.

(3-6 feet.)

MONDAY 11

TUESDAY 12

WEDNESDAY 13

THURSDAY 14

FRIDAY 15 ☾ Last Quarter

SATURDAY 16

SUNDAY 17

Daphne laureola, the spurge laurel,
a member of the Thymelaeaceae family

Thymeleaceae

Daphne Laureola
Spurge Laurel

MONDAY 18

Holiday, USA (Martin Luther King's Birthday)

TUESDAY 19

WEDNESDAY 20

THURSDAY 21

FRIDAY 22 ● New Moon

SATURDAY 23

Chinese New Year

SUNDAY 24

Corylus avellana, the common hazel-nut,
a member of the Betulaceae family

Amentaceae

Corylus Avellana
Common Hazel Nut;

(A shrub or small tree)

week 4 # January 1993

MONDAY 25

TUESDAY 26 *Australia Day*

WEDNESDAY 27

THURSDAY 28

FRIDAY 29

SATURDAY 30 ☽ First Quarter

SUNDAY 31

Larix decidua, the European larch,
a member of the Pinaceae family

Coniferae

Larix
Larch

(A tall tree)

MONDAY 1

TUESDAY 2

WEDNESDAY 3

THURSDAY 4

FRIDAY 5

SATURDAY 6 ○ Full Moon   *Holiday NZ (Waitangi Day)*

SUNDAY 7

Helleborus foetidus, the stinking hellebore or setterwort,
a member of the Ranunculaceae family

Ranunculaceae

Helleborus foetidus
Stinking Hellebore,
Setter-wort.

MONDAY 8

TUESDAY 9

WEDNESDAY 10

THURSDAY 11

FRIDAY 12   *Holiday, USA (Lincoln's Birthday)*

SATURDAY 13   ☾ Last Quarter

SUNDAY 14   *St. Valentine's Day*

Salix caprea, the pussy willow,
a member of the Salicaceae family

Amentaceae.

Salix Caprea
Sallow,
Great Willow.

MONDAY	15	*Holiday, USA (Washington's Birthday)*

TUESDAY 16

WEDNESDAY 17

THURSDAY 18

FRIDAY 19

SATURDAY 20

SUNDAY 21 ● New Moon

Euphorbia amygdaloides, the wood spurge,
a member of the Euphorbiaceae family

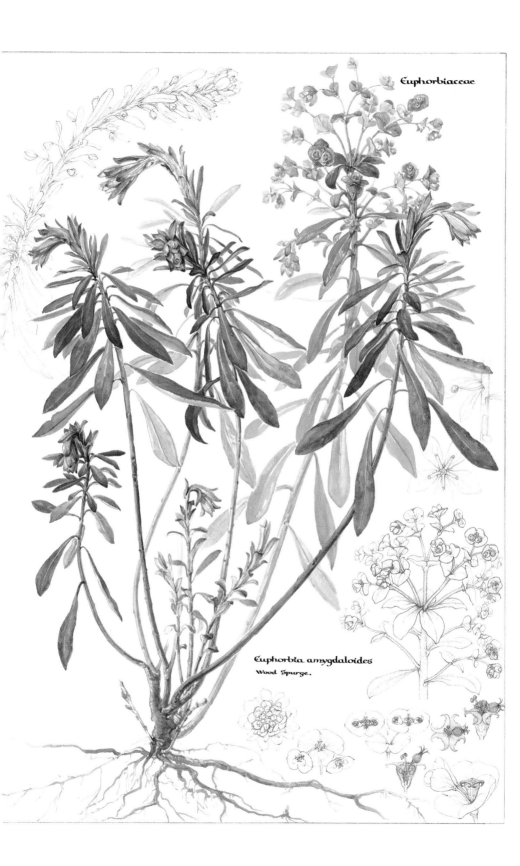

Euphorbiaceae

Euphorbia amygdaloides
Wood Spurge.

MONDAY 22

TUESDAY 23

Shrove Tuesday
Ramadan begins (subject to
sighting of moon)

WEDNESDAY 24

Ash Wednesday

THURSDAY 25

FRIDAY 26

SATURDAY 27

SUNDAY 28

Gentianella (formerly called *Gentiana*) *campestris*, the field gentian,
Gentiana verna, the Spring gentian, *Gentiana pneumonanthe*, the marsh gentian,
members of the Gentianaceae family, and *Crocus vernus* ssp. *vernus*,
the purple crocus, a member of the Iridaceae family

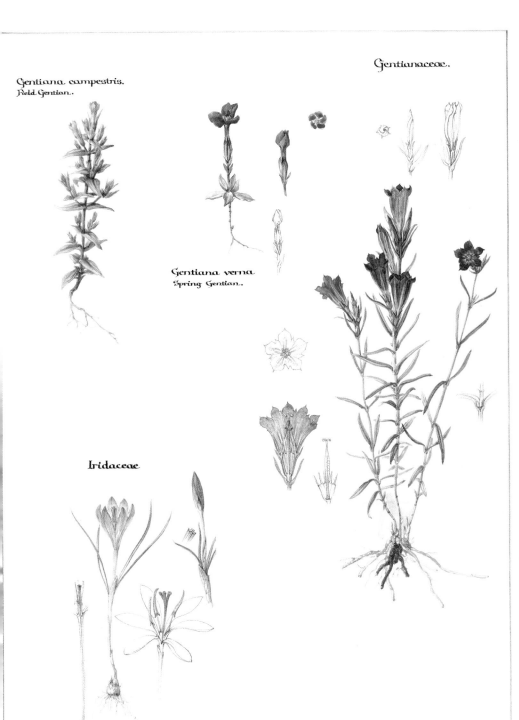

Gentianaceae.

Gentiana campestris.
Field Gentian.

Gentiana verna
Spring Gentian.

Iridaceae

MONDAY	I	☽ First Quarter	*St. David's Day, Wales*

TUESDAY 2

WEDNESDAY 3

THURSDAY 4

FRIDAY 5

SATURDAY 6

SUNDAY 7

Carpinus betulus, the common hornbeam,
a member of the Betulaceae family

Amentaceae

Carpinus Betulus
Hornbeam.

(A small tree)

MONDAY	8	○ Full Moon	*Commonwealth Day*

TUESDAY	9

WEDNESDAY	10

THURSDAY	11

FRIDAY	12

SATURDAY	13

SUNDAY	14

Prunus cerasus, the wild or sour cherry,
a member of the Rosaceae family

Rosaceae

Prunus Cerasus
Wild Cherry.

(A shrub or tree.)

MONDAY	15	☾ Last Quarter

TUESDAY	16

WEDNESDAY	17	*St. Patrick's Day* *Holiday, Northern Ireland and* *Republic of Ireland*

THURSDAY	18

FRIDAY	19

SATURDAY	20	*Vernal Equinox*

SUNDAY	21	*Mothering Sunday (UK)*

Prunus spinosa, the blackthorn or sloe,
a member of the Rosaceae family

MONDAY 22

TUESDAY 23 ● New Moon

WEDNESDAY 24

THURSDAY 25

FRIDAY 26

SATURDAY 27

SUNDAY 28 *British Summer Time begins*

Orchis mascula, Orchis morio, Anacamptis (formerly called *Orchis*) *pyramidalis*,
and *Dactylorhiza majalis* ssp. *praetermissa* (formerly called *Orchis latifolia*),
the early purple, green-winged, pyramidal and marsh orchids,
with *Listera ovata*, the twayblade, members of the Orchidaceae family

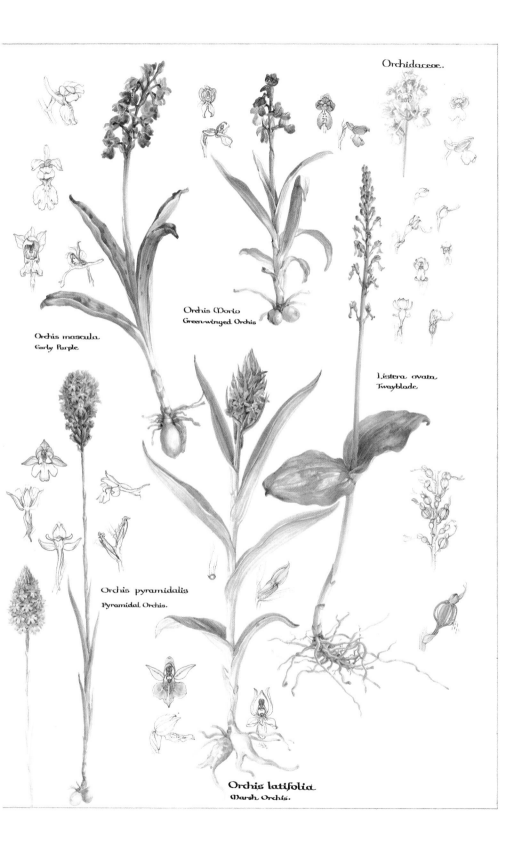

Orchidaceae.

Orchis Morio
Green-winged Orchis

Orchis mascula
Early Purple

Listera ovata
Twayblade

Orchis pyramidalis
Pyramidal Orchis.

Orchis latifolia
Marsh Orchis.

March 1993

MONDAY 29

TUESDAY 30

WEDNESDAY 31 ☽ First Quarter

THURSDAY 1 **April** 1993

FRIDAY 2

SATURDAY 3

SUNDAY 4 *Palm Sunday*

Malus sylvestris (formerly called *Pyrus malus*), the crab-apple,
a member of the Rosaceae family

Rosaceae.

Pyrus Malus
Crab-apple.

MONDAY 5

TUESDAY 6 ○ Full Moon *Passover (Pesach) 1st Day*

WEDNESDAY 7

THURSDAY 8 *Maundy Thursday*

FRIDAY 9 *Good Friday Holiday*

SATURDAY 10

SUNDAY 11 *Easter Day*

Scilla verna, the spring squill, with *Hyacinthoides non-scripta*
(formerly called *Scilla nonscripta*), the bluebell,
members of the Liliaceae family

Liliaceae.

Scilla verna
Spring Squill

Scilla nonscripta
Bluebell.

MONDAY	I2	*Easter Monday*
		Holiday (excluding Scotland and USA)
		Passover (Pesach) 7th Day

TUESDAY I3 ☾ Last Quarter

WEDNESDAY I4

THURSDAY I5

FRIDAY I6

SATURDAY I7

SUNDAY I8

Ribes uva-crispa (formerly called *R. grossularia*), the gooseberry,
a member of the Grossulariaceae family

Ribesiaceae

Ribes Grossularia
Gooseberry.

April *1993*

MONDAY **19**

TUESDAY **20**

WEDNESDAY **21** ● New Moon   *Birthday of Queen Elizabeth II*

THURSDAY **22**

FRIDAY **23**   *St. George's Day, England*

SATURDAY **24**

SUNDAY **25**   *Anzac Day, Australia, NZ*

Vinca minor and *Vinca major*, the lesser and greater periwinkles,
members of the Apocynaceae family

Apocynaceae

Vinca minor
Lesser Periwinkle.

Vinca major
Greater Periwinkle.

April 1993

MONDAY 26

___

TUESDAY 27

___

WEDNESDAY 28

___

THURSDAY 29 ☽ First Quarter

___

FRIDAY 30

___

SATURDAY 1 **May** 1993

___

SUNDAY 2

___

Smyrnium olusatrum, alexanders,
a member of the Umbelliferae family

Umbelliferae

Smyrnium Olusatrum
Alexanders.
(2 to 4 feet.)

week 18 May 1993

MONDAY 3
May Day Holiday, UK (exc. Scotland)
Spring Holiday, Scotland

TUESDAY 4

WEDNESDAY 5

THURSDAY 6 ○ Full Moon

FRIDAY 7

SATURDAY 8

SUNDAY 9

Cytisus scoparius, the common broom,
a member of the Leguminosae family

Papilionaceae.

Cytisus scoparius
Common Broom.

MONDAY 10

_____

TUESDAY 11

_____

WEDNESDAY 12

_____

THURSDAY 13 ☾ Last Quarter

_____

FRIDAY 14

_____

SATURDAY 15

_____

SUNDAY 16

_____

Polygonatum multiflorum, common Solomon's seal,
with *Convallaria majalis*, lily of the valley,
members of the Liliaceae family

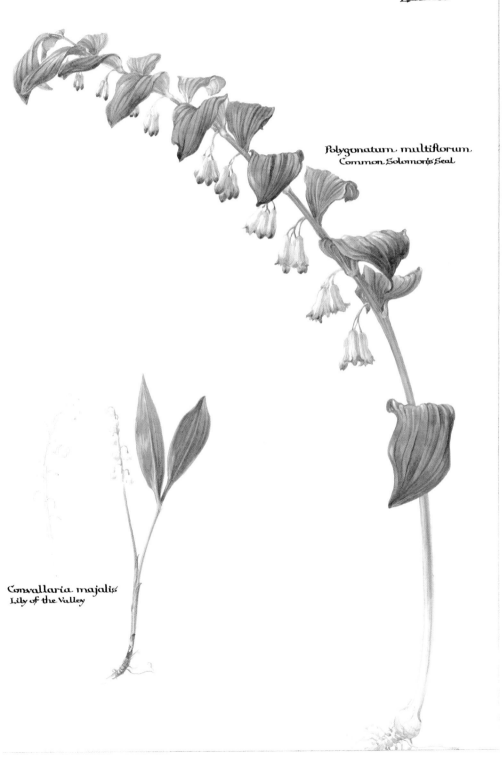

Liliaceae

Polygonatum multiflorum
Common Solomon's Seal

Convallaria majalis
Lily of the Valley

May *1993*

MONDAY **17**

TUESDAY **18**

WEDNESDAY **19**

THURSDAY **20**   *Ascension Day*

FRIDAY **21**   ● New Moon

SATURDAY **22**

SUNDAY **23**

Potentilla reptans, creeping cinquefoil, and *Potentilla anserina*, silverweed,
members of the Rosaceae family

Rosaceae

Potentilla reptans
Creeping Cinquefoil.

MONDAY	24	*Holiday, Canada (Victoria Day)*

TUESDAY	25	

WEDNESDAY	26	*Jewish Feast of Weeks (Shavuot)*

THURSDAY	27	

FRIDAY	28	☽ First Quarter

SATURDAY	29	

SUNDAY	30	*Whit Sunday*

Viburnum opulus, the guelder-rose,
a member of the Caprifoliaceae family

Caprifoliaceae.

Viburnum Opulus
Guelder-Rose

(A small tree)

May *1993*

MONDAY **3 1**

TUESDAY **1** **June** *1993*

WEDNESDAY **2**

THURSDAY **3**

FRIDAY **4** ○ Full Moon

SATURDAY **5**

SUNDAY **6**

Trinity Sunday

Lamium galeobdolon, yellow archangel,
with *Lamium album* and *Lamium purpureum*, the white and red dead-nettle,
members of the Labiatae family

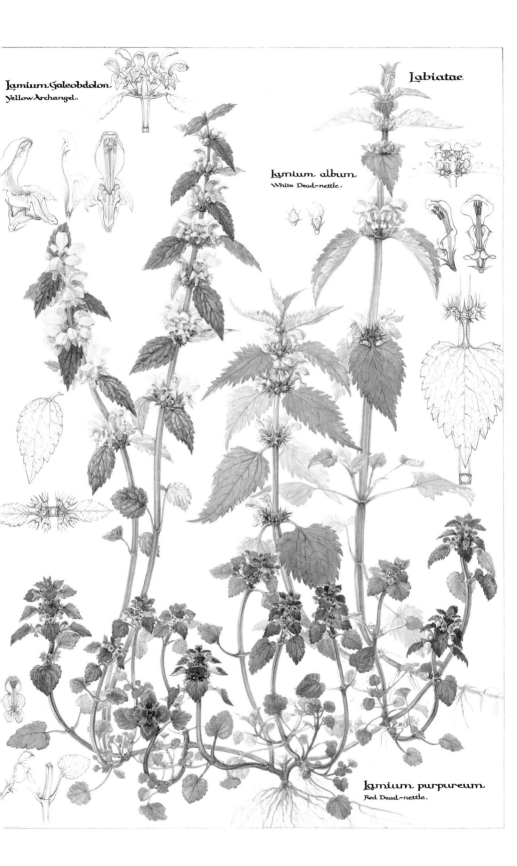

Lamium Galeobdolon.
Yellow Archangel.

Labiatae.

Lamium album
White Dead-nettle.

Lamium purpureum
Red Dead-nettle.

MONDAY 7

Holiday, Republic of Ireland
Holiday, New Zealand
(Queen's Birthday)

TUESDAY 8

WEDNESDAY 9

THURSDAY 10

Corpus Christi

FRIDAY 11

SATURDAY 12 ☾ Last Quarter

The Queen's Official Birthday
(subject to confirmation)

SUNDAY 13

Anchusa arvensis (here called *A. officinalis*), bugloss,
with *Borago officinalis*, common borage,
members of the Boraginaceae family

Boragineae.

Anchusa officinalis
Common Alkanet

Borago officinalis
Common Borage

MONDAY 14

TUESDAY 15

WEDNESDAY 16

THURSDAY 17

FRIDAY 18

SATURDAY 19

SUNDAY 20 ● New Moon   *Father's Day (UK)*

Rosa pimpinellifolia, the Scotch or burnet rose (top left),
with *Rosa eglanteria*, sweetbriar or eglantine (top right)
and *Rosa canina*, the dog rose (bottom), members of the Rosaceae family

MONDAY	21	*Summer Solstice* *Islamic New Year (subject* *to sighting of moon)*

TUESDAY 22

WEDNESDAY 23

THURSDAY 24

FRIDAY 25

SATURDAY 26 ☽ First Quarter

SUNDAY 27

Hyoscyamus niger, henbane,
a member of the Solanaceae family

Solanaceae.

Hyoscyamus niger
Henbane

MONDAY   28

TUESDAY   29

WEDNESDAY 30

THURSDAY I   **July** 1993   *Holiday Canada (Canada Day)*

FRIDAY   2

SATURDAY 3   ○ Full Moon

SUNDAY   4   *Independence Day, USA*

Geranium sylvaticum, the wood crane's-bill,
a member of the Geraniaceae family

Geraniaceae

Geranium sylvaticum
Wood Crane's-Bill

MONDAY 5 *Holiday USA*

TUESDAY 6

WEDNESDAY 7

THURSDAY 8

FRIDAY 9

SATURDAY 10

SUNDAY 11 ☾ Last Quarter

Verbascum thapsus, the common or great mullein or flannel plant,
a member of the Scrophulariaceae family

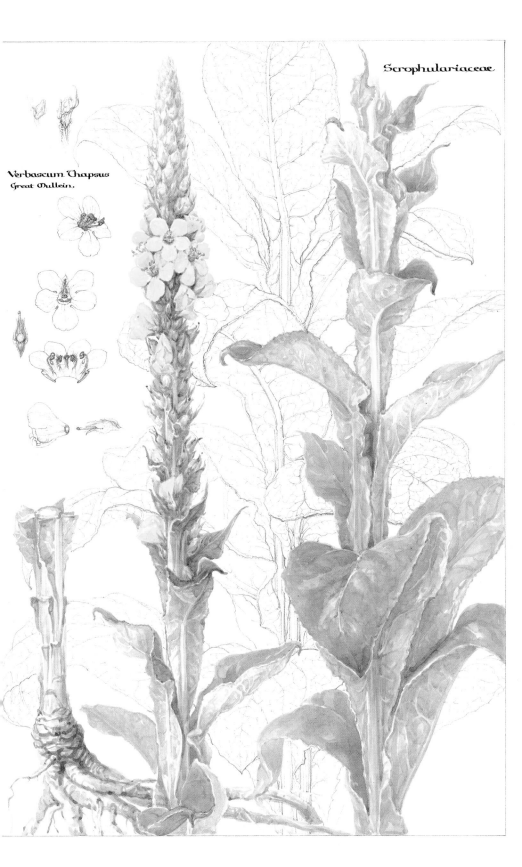

Scrophulariaceae

Verbascum Thapsus
Great Mullein.

MONDAY I 2   *Holiday, N. Ireland (Battle*
                               of the Boyne)

TUESDAY I 3

WEDNESDAY I4

THURSDAY I 5   *St. Swithin's Day*

FRIDAY I 6

SATURDAY I 7

SUNDAY I 8

Campanula latifolia, the giant bellflower,
a member of the Campanulaceae family

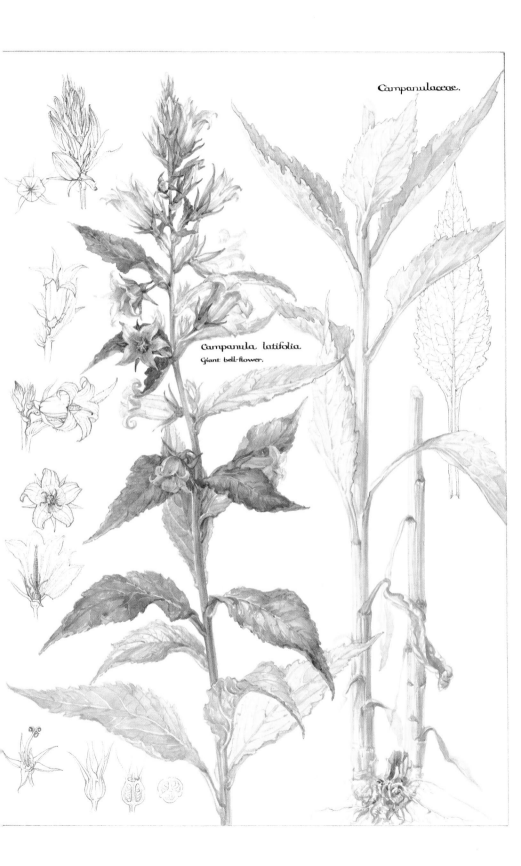

Campanulaceae.

Campanula latifolia
Giant bell-flower.

July 1993

MONDAY 19 ● New Moon

TUESDAY 20

WEDNESDAY 21

THURSDAY 22

FRIDAY 23

SATURDAY 24

SUNDAY 25

Senecio integrifolius (formerly called *S. campestris*),
and *Senecio jacobaea*, the field fleawort and ragwort,
members of the Compositae family

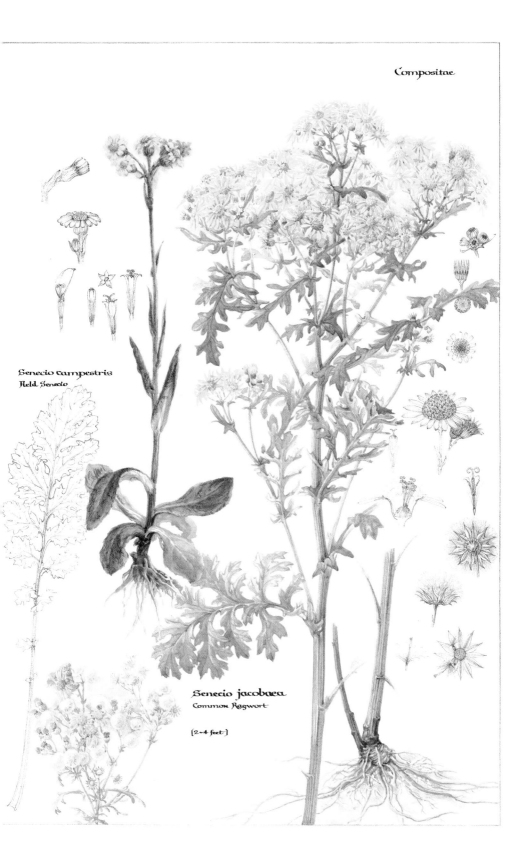

Compositae

Senecio campestris
Field Senecio

Senecio jacobaea
Common Ragwort

[2~4 feet]

MONDAY 26 ☽ First Quarter

TUESDAY 27

WEDNESDAY 28

THURSDAY 29

FRIDAY 30

SATURDAY 31

SUNDAY 1 **August** 1993

Angelica sylvestris, the wild angelica,
a member of the Umbelliferae family

Umbelliferae.

Angelica sylvestris.
Wild Angelica.

(Height –3 to 5 feet.)

week 31 # August 1993

MONDAY 2 ○ Full Moon   *Summer Holiday, Scotland*
                                          Holiday, Republic of Ireland

---

TUESDAY 3

WEDNESDAY 4

THURSDAY 5

FRIDAY 6

SATURDAY 7

SUNDAY 8

Cichorium intybus, chicory or succory,
a member of the Compositae family

Compositae

Cichorium Intybus
Chicory
Succory

(1 to 4 ft. high.)

August 1993

MONDAY 9

TUESDAY 10   ☾ Last Quarter

WEDNESDAY 11

THURSDAY 12

FRIDAY 13

SATURDAY 14

SUNDAY 15

Dipsacus fullonum (formerly called *D. sylvestris*), the wild teasel,
a member of the Dipsacaceae family

Dipsaceae.

Dipsacus sylvestris
Wild Teasel.

{Height:- 4 or 5 feet.}

August 1993

MONDAY 16

TUESDAY 17 ● New Moon

WEDNESDAY 18

THURSDAY 19

FRIDAY 20

SATURDAY 21

SUNDAY 22

Mimulus guttatus, the yellow mimulus, with *Mimulus guttatus × luteus*,
members of the Scrophulariaceae family

Scrophulariaceae

Mimulus guttatus
yellow Mimulus

August 1993

MONDAY **23**

TUESDAY **24** ☽ First Quarter

WEDNESDAY **25**

THURSDAY **26**

FRIDAY **27**

SATURDAY **28**

SUNDAY **29**

Salvia verbenaca, vervain or wild clary,
a member of the Labiatae family

Labiatae

Salvia Verbenaca
Clary.

August 1993

MONDAY 30   *Summer Holiday, UK (exc. Scotland)*

TUESDAY 31

WEDNESDAY 1   **September** 1993
○ Full Moon

THURSDAY 2

FRIDAY 3

SATURDAY 4

SUNDAY 5

Sedum anglicum, English stonecrop, *Sedum fabaria,*
Sedum album, white stonecrop, *Sedum acre*, wall pepper or biting stonecrop,
and *Sedum telephium*, orpine, members of the Crassulaceae family

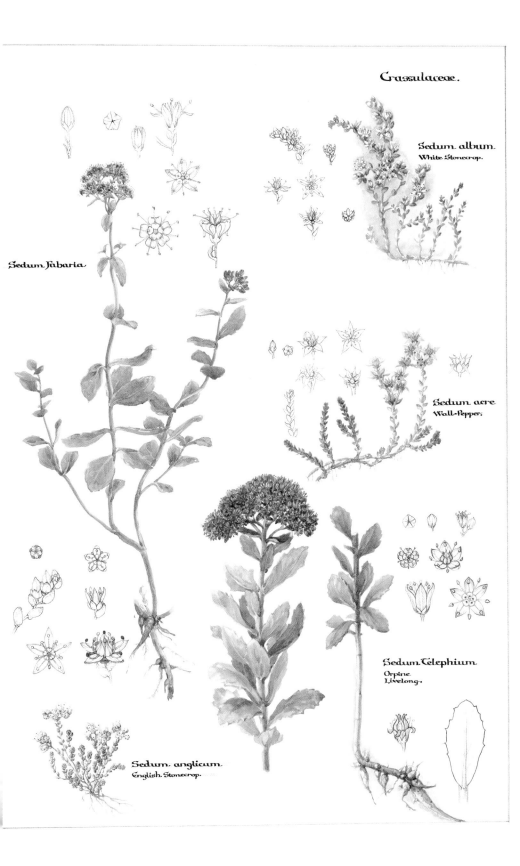

Crassulaceae.

Sedum album.
White Stonecrop.

Sedum Fabaria

Sedum acre
Wall-Pepper.

Sedum Telephium
Orpine.
Livelong.

Sedum anglicum
English Stonecrop.

September 1993

MONDAY 6

Holiday, Canada (Labour Day), USA (Labor Day)

TUESDAY 7

WEDNESDAY 8

THURSDAY 9 ☾ Last Quarter

FRIDAY 10

SATURDAY 11

SUNDAY 12

Nymphaea alba, the white waterlily,
a member of the Nymphaeaceae family

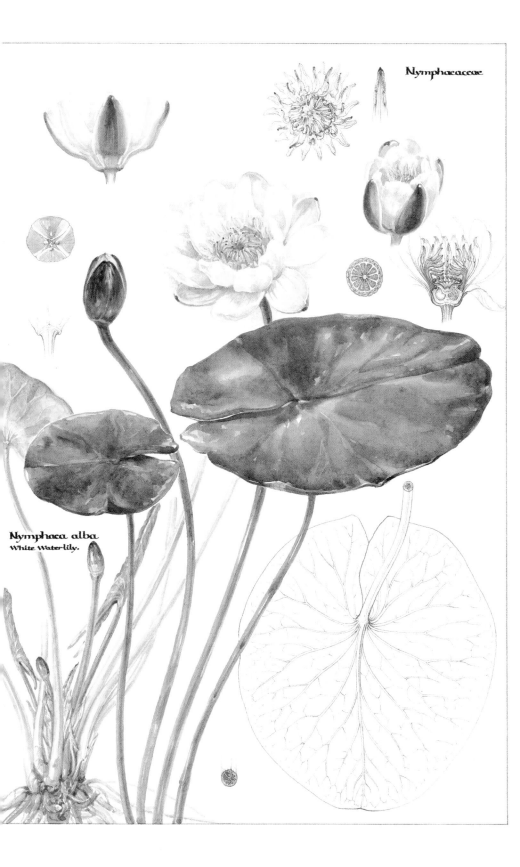

Nymphaeaceae

Nymphaea alba
White Water-lily.

September 1993

MONDAY 13

TUESDAY 14

WEDNESDAY 15

THURSDAY 16 ● New Moon *Jewish New Year (Rosh Hashanah)*

FRIDAY 17

SATURDAY 18

SUNDAY 19

Knautia (formerly called *Scabiosa*) *arvensis*, the field scabious,
a member of the Dipsacaceae family

Dipsacaceae

Scabiosa arvensis
field Scabious

September 1993

MONDAY	20	
TUESDAY	21	
WEDNESDAY	22	☽ First Quarter
THURSDAY	23	*Autumnal Equinox*
FRIDAY	24	
SATURDAY	25	*Jewish Day of Atonement (Yom Kippur)*
SUNDAY	26	

Humulus lupulus, the hop,
a member of the Cannabidaceae family

Urticaceae

Humulus Lupulus
Hop

(Climber 10-20 feet:)

September 1993

MONDAY	27	
TUESDAY	28	
WEDNESDAY	29	*Michaelmas Day*
THURSDAY	30 ○ Full Moon	*Jewish Festival of Tabernacles (Succoth) First Day*
FRIDAY	1 **October** 1993	
SATURDAY	2	
SUNDAY	3	

Sorbus (formerly called *Pyrus*) *aucuparia*, the rowan or mountain ash, a member of the Rosaceae family

Rosaceae

Pyrus Aucuparia
Rowan-tree,
Mountain-Ash.

(A moderate-sized tree.)

MONDAY 4

TUESDAY 5

WEDNESDAY 6

THURSDAY 7   *Jewish Festival of Tabernacles*
                                               (Succoth) Eighth Day

FRIDAY 8   ☾ Last Quarter

SATURDAY 9

SUNDAY 10

Sambucus nigra, the elder and *Viburnum lantana*, the wayfaring tree,
members of the Caprifoliaceae family

Caprifoliaceae

Sambucus nigra
Common Elder

(A small tree)

Viburnum Lantana
Wayfaring-tree

(A large shrub)

October *1993*

MONDAY **11**

Holiday, Canada (Thanksgiving)
Holiday, USA (Columbus Day)

TUESDAY **12**

WEDNESDAY **13**

THURSDAY **14**

FRIDAY **15** ● New Moon

SATURDAY **16**

SUNDAY **17**

Tilia × europea, the common lime,
a member of the Tiliaceae family

Tiliaceae

Tilia europaea
Common lime

(long-lived tree)

October *1993*

MONDAY **18**

TUESDAY **19**

WEDNESDAY **20**

THURSDAY **21**

FRIDAY **22** ☽ First Quarter

SATURDAY **23**

SUNDAY **24**

United Nations' Day
British Summer Time ends
(subject to confirmation)

Tamus communis, the black bryony,
a member of the Dioscoreaceae family

Dioscorideae

Tamus communis
Black Bryony

October *1993*

MONDAY 2 5 *Holiday, (Republic of Ireland)*

TUESDAY 26

WEDNESDAY 27

THURSDAY 28

FRIDAY 29

SATURDAY 3 0 ○ Full Moon

SUNDAY 3 1 *Hallowe'en*

A hybrid between *Quercus robur*, the common or pedunculate oak,
and *Q. petraea*, members of the Fagaceae family

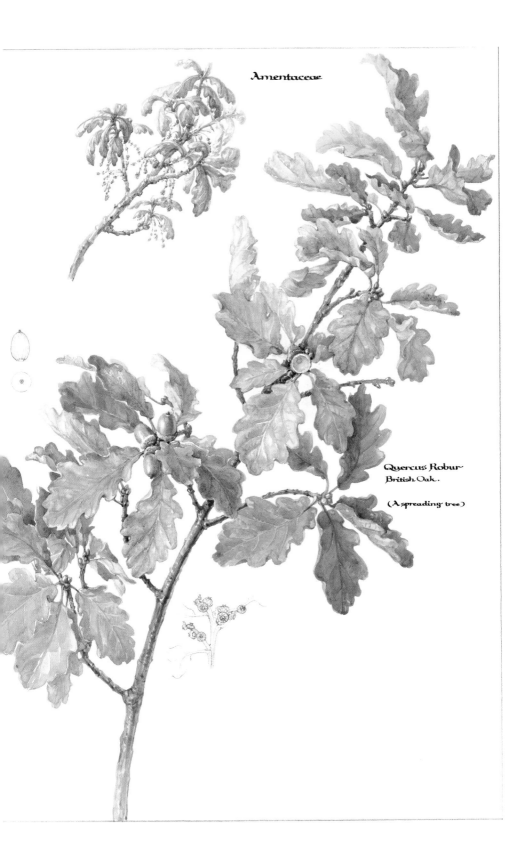

Amentaceæ

Quercus Robur
British Oak.

(A spreading tree)

November *1993*

MONDAY	**I**	*All Saints' Day*

TUESDAY	**2**	

WEDNESDAY	**3**	

THURSDAY	**4**	

FRIDAY	**5**	*Guy Fawkes' Day, UK*

SATURDAY	**6**	

SUNDAY	**7**	☾ Last Quarter

Crataegus, the hawthorn, may or whitethorn,
a member of the Rosaceae family
The blossom is that of *C. monogyna*
and the fruit that of *C. laevigata* (formerly called *C. oxyacantha*)

Rosaceae.

Crataegus Oxyacantha
Hawthorn.
May
Whitethorn.

week 45 # November *1993*

MONDAY	8

TUESDAY	9

WEDNESDAY	10

THURSDAY	11

Holiday, Canada (Remembrance day)
Holiday, USA (Armistice/Veterans' Day)

FRIDAY	12

SATURDAY	13	● New Moon

SUNDAY	14

Remembrance Sunday

Berberis vulgaris, the barberry,
a member of the Berberidaceae family

Berberidaceae

Berberis vulgaris
Barberry.

[Shrub 6~8 feet]

November 1993

MONDAY **15**

TUESDAY **16**

WEDNESDAY **17**

THURSDAY **18**

FRIDAY **19**

SATURDAY **20**

SUNDAY **21**   ☽ First Quarter

Iris foetidissima, the fetid iris, gladdon, or roast beef plant,
a member of the Iridaceae family

Iridaceae

Iris foetidissima
fetid Iris
Gladdon
Roastbeef-plant

November 1993

MONDAY 22

TUESDAY 23

WEDNESDAY 24

THURSDAY 25 *Holiday, USA (Thanksgiving Day)*

FRIDAY 26

SATURDAY 27

SUNDAY 28 *Advent Sunday*

Taxus baccata, the common yew,
a member of the Taxaceae family

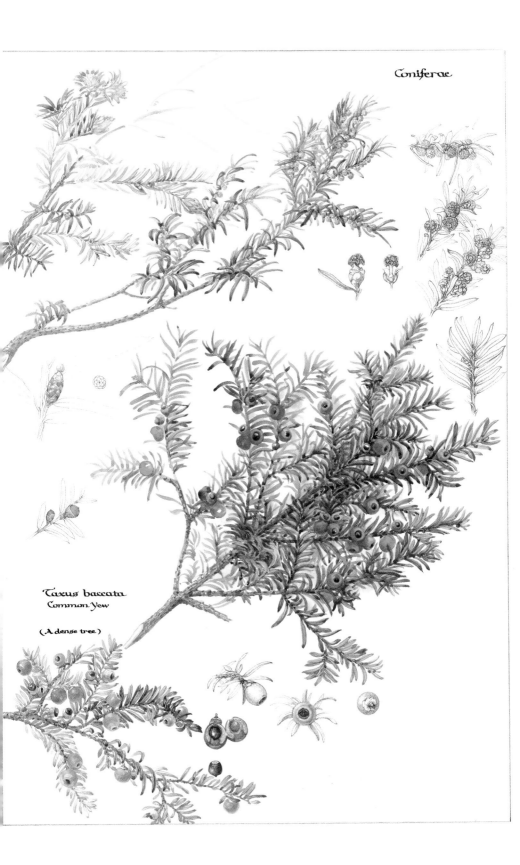

Coniferae

Taxus baccata
Common Yew

(A dense tree)

November *1993*

MONDAY   **29**   ○ Full Moon

TUESDAY   **30**   *St. Andrew's Day, Scotland*

WEDNESDAY   **1**   **December** *1993*

THURSDAY   **2**

FRIDAY   **3**

SATURDAY   **4**

SUNDAY   **5**

Fagus sylvatica, the beech,
a member of the Fagaceae family

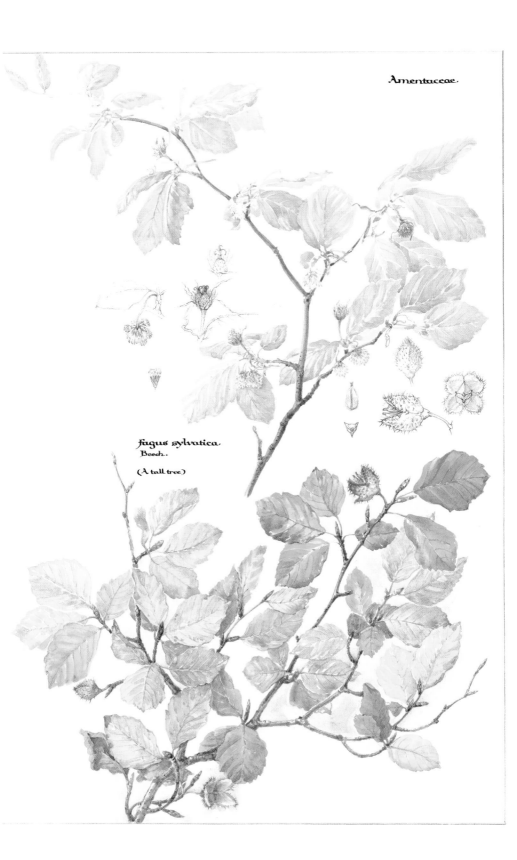

Amentaceae.

fagus sylvatica
Beech.

(A tall tree)

December 1993

MONDAY **6** ☽ Last Quarter

TUESDAY **7**

WEDNESDAY **8**

THURSDAY **9** *Chanukah*

FRIDAY **10**

SATURDAY **11**

SUNDAY **12**

Euonymus europaeus, the spindle tree,
a member of the Celastraceae family

Celastraceae.

Euonymus europaeus
Common Spindle-tree.

MONDAY	13	● New Moon
TUESDAY	14	
WEDNESDAY	15	
THURSDAY	16	
FRIDAY	17	
SATURDAY	18	
SUNDAY	19	

Viscum album, the mistletoe,
a member of the Viscaceae family

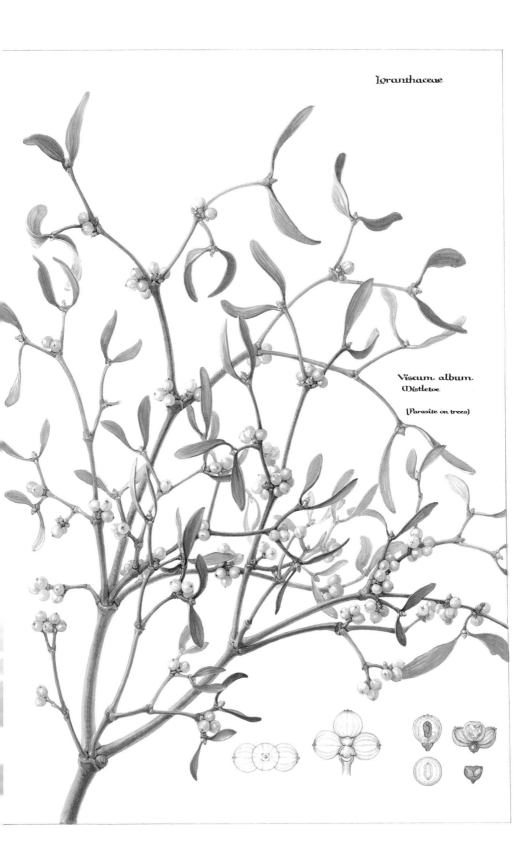

Loranthaceae

Viscum album
Mistletoe

(Parasite on trees)

December 1993

MONDAY   20   ☽ First Quarter

TUESDAY   21   *Winter Solstice*

WEDNESDAY   22

THURSDAY   23

FRIDAY   24   *Christmas Eve*

SATURDAY   25   *Christmas Day*

SUNDAY   26   *Boxing Day, St. Stephen's Day*

Ilex aquifolium, the holly,
a member of the Aquifoliaceae family

Aquifoliaceae

Ilex Aquifolium.
Holly.

[Evergreen Shrub or Tree]

MONDAY 27

Holiday, UK (inc. Scotland),
Canada and USA
Holiday, Republic of Ireland

TUESDAY 28 ○ Full Moon

Holiday, UK (inc. Scotland),
Canada

WEDNESDAY 29

THURSDAY 30

FRIDAY 31

SATURDAY 1 **January** 1994

New Year's Day Holiday

SUNDAY 2

Clematis vitalba, traveller's joy or old man's beard,
a member of the Ranunculaceae family

Ranunculaceae

Clematis Vitalba
Traveller's Joy
Old Man's Beard

European National Holidays 1993
Holidays that fall on a Sunday are not included

AUSTRIA   January 1, 6; April 12; May 1, 20, 31; June 10; October 26; November 1; December 8, 25

BELGIUM   January 1; April 12; May 1, 20, 31; July 21; November 1; December 25

DENMARK   January 1; April 8, 9, 12; May 7, 20, 31; June 5; December 25

FINLAND   January 1, 6; April 9, 12; May 1, 20; June 26; November 6; December 6, 25

FRANCE   January 1; April 12; May 1, 8, 20, 31; July 14; November 1, 11; December 25

GERMANY   January 1; April, 12; May 1, 20, 31; November 17; December 25

GREECE   January 1, 6; March 1, 25; April 16, 19; May 1; June 7; October 28; December 25

ITALY   January 1, 6; April 12; May 1; November 1; December 8, 25

LUXEMBOURG   January 1; April 12; May 1, 20, 31; June 23; November 1; December 25

NETHERLANDS   January 1; April 12, 30; May 20, 31; December 25

NORWAY   January 1; April 8, 9, 12; May 1, 17, 20, 31; December 25

PORTUGAL   January 1; February 23; April 9; May 1; June 10; October 5; December 1, 8, 25

SPAIN   January 1, 6; March 19; April 8, 9, 12; May 1, 20; October 12; November 1;
                 December 8, 25

SWEDEN   January 1, 6; April 9, 12; May 1, 20, 31; June 26; November 6; December 25

SWITZERLAND   January 1; April 9, 12; May 1, 20, 31; December 25